WORKSHOP PARTICIPANT GUIDE

Making *the* Connections

© 2008 The Biblical Worldview Institute
A Division of Cascade Christian Schools
815 21st Street S. E. • Puyallup, WA 98372
253.841.1776 • www.biblicalworldviewinstitute.org

We gratefully acknowledge the following source of video used in accordance with the Fair Use Rule in this workshop for the educational purpose and intent of this course:

American Visions: The Wilderness and the West, The History of American Art and Architecture (Volume 3), BBC Worldwide Americas, Inc., 1996.

BIBLICAL WORLDVIEW INSTITUTE

Dear Participant,

Welcome to *"Making the Connections: Biblical Worldview Integration in the Classroom"* educational training workshop. We are excited that you are joining thousands of others who have embarked on this transformational worldview journey.

We know you would agree that one of the greatest challenges facing Christian educators is the task of giving the next generation an understanding of what a biblical worldview is, and then teaching them to *"make connections"* between that worldview and every subject taught in school.

In this workshop, we will be providing you with training in how to plan and implement effective biblical worldview integration in your lesson plans by using a very practical tool called the *"Biblical Worldview Integration Planner"* which you can begin using in your classroom immediately!

This Participant Guide is a helpful tool to facilitate your workshop experience and will provide a quick reference after you have completed the workshop.

Rest assured that whether you are a seasoned veteran or just taking your first steps, we are here for you!

Sincerely,

The staff at the Biblical Worldview Institute

815 21st Street Southeast • Puyallup, Washington 98372 • 253-841-1776

CONTENTS

What Shapes Culture?

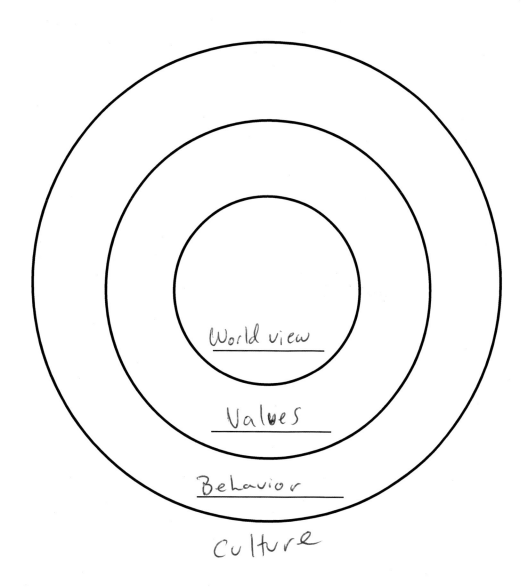

World view

Values

Behavior

Culture

WORLDVIEW:

"A comprehensive _____framework_____ that helps us to _____interpret_____ what we see and experience and also gives us direction in the_____choices_____ that we make as we live out our days"

~ Richard Wright

A.   Form a "huddle-group" with a maximum of three people. Your group will have approximately six minutes to complete this exercise.

B.   Select a facilitator and have this person read the following aloud to your group:

Imagine yourself suddenly entering life as a full-grown adult. You not only see the sky for the first time, hear the sound of birds, and watch trees bending in the wind, but you also observe other people walking, talking, driving cars and busying themselves at their jobs and leisure activities. You notice various buildings, like post offices, gas stations, schools and courthouses. You see farms and watch ships unloading at the waterfront.

You have no prior knowledge of anything, but oddly enough, you can understand the language being spoken. You can also read and write. You watch television programs, including CNN and 1950's sitcom re-runs. You read the newspaper, listen to the radio, and spend hours in the public library trying to figure out where you came from, how everything got here, what the purpose of it all may be, and what keeps it going.

You want to know the meaning of your existence [if any], as well as the significance of life around you. You wonder if there is a "Higher Being," or "God," behind it all. You wonder why humans behave the way they do, and you try to figure out what the "rules" are for human behavior and where the rules come from.

At the end of thirty days, you make a list of the most basic questions you'd like to have answered. You place your questions into five categories, namely: "God," "Creation," "Humanity," "Moral Order," and "Purpose."

Thinking Exercise #1

As a group, our task is to identify as many basic questions as we can, in each of the five categories given. (Some questions may fit more than one category.)

QUESTIONS ABOUT GOD:

Is there a higher being?
Where is he/she?
What control does she have?
Where did she come from?

QUESTIONS ABOUT CREATION:

How was it made?   Why is it created the way
Who created it?   it is?
Why was it created?
Why is Jared here?

QUESTIONS ABOUT HUMANITY:

Are we inherintly good or bad?
Why is Jared here?
What distinguishes animals & humans?

QUESTIONS ABOUT MORAL ORDER:

Who determines right and wrong?
Why are there rules?

QUESTIONS ABOUT PURPOSE:

What is my purpose?
What is purpose of life?

A working definition of "WORLDVIEW"

A worldview is a person's mental concept
of the "big picture" of reality,
as shaped by conscious beliefs
or subconscious assumptions about

_____

_____

_____

_____

_____

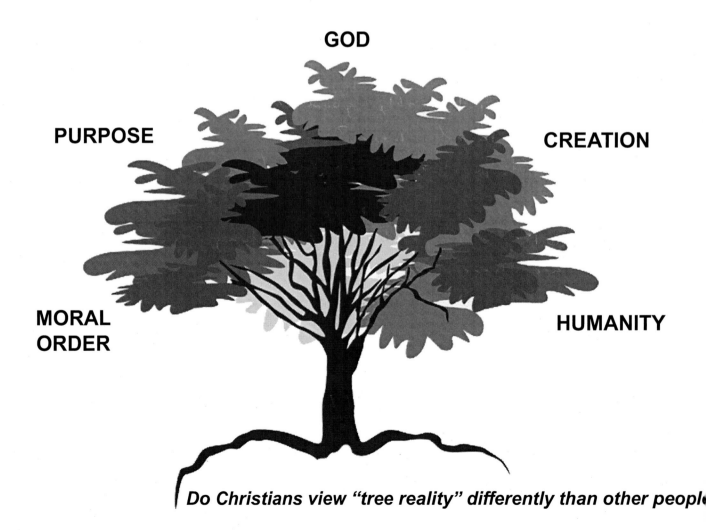

GOD

PURPOSE

CREATION

MORAL ORDER

HUMANITY

Do Christians view "tree reality" differently than other people

Your huddle-group will have approximately six minutes to complete this exercise. Follow these instructions:

Does a biblical worldview shape a person's view of what is "really real" about math?

Your task is to identify ways mathematics "connects" with the biblical concept of God, the biblical concept of Creation, the biblical concept of Humanity, the biblical concept of Moral Order, and the biblical concept of Purpose.

In the space below, list as many connections as possible. Some connections may be fitting for more than one category.

Connections between math and God:

Truths

Connections between math and Creation:

Creation is built on mathematical concepts.

Connections between math and Humanity:

Age → respect   calender → organization

Connections between math and Moral Order:

Connections between math and Purpose:

...Earth's crammed with heaven,

And every common bush afire with God,

And only he who sees takes off his shoes —

The rest sit around it and pluck blackberries.

From "Aurora Leigh" by Elizabeth Barrett Browning

"Beauty, power, order, symmetry, infinitude - though these characteristics of mathematics are there for anyone, the Christian sees them in their proper light as reflections of God's attributes... the teacher periodically identifies these qualities for the students and reminds them that what they are beholding are beams of God's glory. "

"If mathematics is the basic language of creation, its nature is to reveal God, and its purpose is to glorify God, it must be desecularized. That is, the patina of secularization with which mathematics has become encrusted must be polished away so that its true God-reflecting nature shines through. Nearly always students mush have this done for them by their teacher until the idea takes root in their minds."

Larry Zimmerman,
Truth and the Transcendent

A worldview is a frame of reference by

which we _____ and

_____ reality.

———————————————————

Our challenge is to help students to "make the

connections" between academic subjects and

the biblical frame of reference, thus "reinvesting

facts with their _____ meaning."

Drivers of Christian Education

- The biblical frame of reference ought to govern a Christian's perception of reality for every subject.

- If the biblical worldview is not shaping our students' perception of reality, other worldviews will.

- Our students' worldviews will be shaped by DESIGN or by DEFAULT!

Biblical worldview integration

means _____ **between**

academic content and the bigger picture of

the _biblical worldview._

Watch the video example and determine:

1. What is this teacher's academic lesson objective/outcome?

2. Which biblical worldview component is this teacher "connecting" with the subject matter?

    God   Creation   Humanity   Moral Order   Purpose

Step 1
Beginning the Lesson Plan

1. Fill in reference information in preparation for planning.

2. Determine the subject you wish to integrate with a biblical worldview, and note the references you will use.

Step 2
Lesson or Unit Objective/Outcome

1. Decide on the main point of the lesson:

2. Determine the highest _____ _____ of student learning.

Six Levels of Thought ("Bloom's Taxonomy")

1. _____ = *recall of information:*

   "The students will recite the 5th Commandment (Honor your father and mother...)."

2. _____ = *understanding meanings:*

   "The students will paraphrase the 5th Commandment in their own words."

3. _____ = *applying concepts to new situations:*

   "The students will relate how they applied the 5th Commandment to their lives this week."

4. _____ = *analyzing, comparing, contrasting or making inferences:*

   "The students will explain what sets the 5th Commandment apart from the other 9 Commandments."

5. _____ =*creating original ideas or relating knowledge from different spheres:*

   "The students will formulate a theory that would explain the relationship between the violation of the 5th Commandment and the lack of self-control in school settings."

6. _____ = *making assessments or discriminating between ideas:*

   "The students will assess the long term cultural effects of violating the 5th Commandment."

THINKING LEVELS
(Bloom's Taxonomy)

Knowledge: Observation and recall of information. Students will *list, tell, identify, show, label, collect, examine, tabulate, quote, or name, etc.*

Comprehension: Understanding information, grasping meanings, translating knowledge into new contexts, interpreting facts, comparing and contrasting, ordering, grouping, inferring causes and predicting consequences. Students will *summarize, describe, associate, distinguish, estimate, differentiate, explain in their own words, discuss or articulate, etc.*

Application: Using previously learned information to solve problems or applying skills or concepts to new situations. Students will *apply, demonstrate, calculate, complete, illustrate, show, solve, modify, relate, change, classify or experiment, etc.*

Analysis: Seeing patterns, organizing parts, recognizing hidden meanings or identifying various components. Students will *analyze, separate, order, connect, classify, arrange, divide, compare, contrast, select, determine, decipher, predict, interpret or infer, etc.*

Synthesis: Using old ideas to create new or original ones, generalizing from given facts, relating knowledge from several different spheres, predicting or drawing conclusions. Students will *combine, integrate, modify, rearrange, substitute, plan, create, design, invent, compose, formulate or generalize, etc.*

Evaluation: Comparing and discriminating between ideas, assessing the value of theories or presentations, making choices based on reasoned arguments, verifying the value of evidence or recognizing subjectivity. Students will *assess, decide, rank, grade, test, measure, recommend, convince, select, judge, defend, discriminate, support or conclude, etc.*

Do's and Don'ts when Writing the Lesson Objective/Outcome

DO:

- Use few words, in one complete sentence.
- Articulate the main academic objective to be reached by the end of the lesson.
- Specify the highest thinking level (TL) you want student to employ and underline it.
- Identify the basic academic content (AC) you are dealing with in the lesson and circle it.

DON'T:

- Mix biblical interaction into the academic objective.

Step 3: Academic Lesson Plan

1. **Set:**
   Prepares or gets students "set" for learning about the academic subject.

2. **Delivery:**
   Basic outline of the lesson plan or a step-by-step plan of what will be accomplished in the lesson.

3. **Closing:**
   Concludes the lesson with review of key points of the lesson.

Findlay's Academic Objective:

Students will be able to interpret "The Pasture" as a possible invitation to take time to enjoy the simple things in life like water springs and calves.

The Pasture

I'm going out to clean the pasture spring;

I'll only stop to rake the leaves away

(And wait to watch the water clear, I may):

I sha'n't be gone long. — You come too.

I'm going out to fetch the little calf

That's standing by the mother. It's so young,

It totters when she licks it with her tongue.

I sha'n't be gone long. — You come too.

~Robert Frost

Step 4: Biblical Worldview Component

How does _____ connect with the bigger picture of

(the academic content)

God, Creation, Humanity, Moral Order, and Purpose?

Defining the 5 Biblical Worldview Components

GOD: *Has to do with the **nature, character and role of God.***

CREATION: *Has to do with **what is made and sustained by God.***

HUMANITY: *Has to do with **who and what humans are.***

MORAL ORDER: *Has to do with **moral behavior and responsibility.***

PURPOSE: *Has to do with the **intention or meaning of all that exists.***

Five Boxcars
and Cargo of Core Biblical Truth

(For Scriptural references, see the "Making The Connections" text, Chapter 4.)

Has to do with the nature, character and role of God

- God is a divine Person, with mind, emotion and free will.

- God is omnipotent, omniscient and omnipresent.

- God is sovereign over all things.

- God communicates with humanity.

- God is faultless in judgment, infinite in mercy and perfect in justice.

Has to do with what is made and sustained by God.

- All things have been created and are continually sustained by God.

- The realm of creation belongs entirely to God.

- The created realm includes physical and spiritual realities, as well as temporal and eternal realities.

- Creation has been plagued by sin since the Fall of humanity.

- The created realm has not been forsaken by God, in spite of the Fall.

HUMANITY

Has to do with who and what humans are.

- Humans were created by God's choice and design.
- Man and woman were specially created in the likeness and image of God so they could engage in His purposes.
- People are alienated from God through sin.
- Humans can be restored to a right relationship with God through Christ.
- All humans experience physical death, followed by eternal fellowship with God or eternal separation from Him.

MORAL ORDER

Has to do with moral behavior and responsibility.

- Moral order is determined by God, not invented by humans.
- The moral order of God is non-optional and non-negotiable.
- Moral order, when violated, requires consequences.
- Moral order is clarified through biblical examples of good and evil.
- Moral order is upheld through God's ordained institutions of family, church and state.

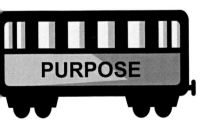

PURPOSE

Has to do with the intention or meaning of all that exists.

- The First Commission God gave to humanity [Gen. 1:26-28] was that of rulership over the earth.
- The will of God is to be done on earth as it is in heaven.
- The function of believers in Christ is to be the "salt of the earth" and the "light of the world."
- The purpose of all things centers in Christ.
- The Great Commission [Matthew 28:18-20] is still in place.

Develop two additional Specific Biblical Truth (SBT) statements for the worldview component of your choice on pages 14 and 15.

Worldview component: _____

Specific Biblical Truth:

Worldview component: _____

Specific Biblical Truth:

Extract Specific Biblical Truths (SBTs) from **one of the two** Scripture portions below using as many of the five worldview components as you can.

"Be anxious for nothing, but in everything by prayer and supplication, with thanksgiving, let your requests be made known to God." (Philippians 4:6)

- **God:**

- **Creation:**

- **Humanity:**

- **Moral Order:**

- **Purpose:**

"When I consider Your heavens, the work of Your fingers, the moon and the stars, which You have ordained, what is man that You care for him? For You have made him a little lower than the angels, and You have crowned him with glory and honor. You have made him to have dominion over the works of Your hands; You have put all things under his feet." (Psalm 8:3-6)

- **God:**

- **Creation:**

- **Humanity:**

- **Moral Order:**

- **Purpose:**

In the examples of BWI Planners given on pages 56, 60, and 62 in the white pages of the text [*Making the Connections*, Chapter 8], **compare Step 4 with Step 5**, as follows:

a) Notice which of the 5 Biblical Worldview Components has been selected in Step 4, and

b) Note how the verbiage in Step 5 answers the question **"what about?"** in reference to the worldview component selected in Step 4.

For example, if the teacher has selected **"Moral Order"** in **Step 4**, note how the statement in **Step 5** answers the question: *"What about Moral Order?"*

Answer the Focus Question for all 5 BW Components

Choose One Worldview Component

Write the Specific Biblical Truth

Step 5: Specific Biblical Truth(s)

Making the connection with the Academic Lesson Plan

Step 6: Biblical Worldview Integration Objective

Findlay's *Integration Objective:*

The students will understand that creation is designed to give pleasure to the sight, through the process of reading "The Pasture" and discussing its theme of taking time to enjoy the simple things in life.

Things to look for in an *Integration Objective:*

1. Does the **THINKING LEVEL (TL)** match (or not supersede) the thinking level of the Academic Objective determined in Step 2?

2. Is the **SPECIFIC BIBLICAL TRUTH (SBT)** restated, as determined in Step 5?

3. Does the **ACADEMIC CONTENT (AC)** match the academic content determined in Step 2?

Step 7: Integration Plan

ASK YOURSELF:

- How will you "connect" the specific academic outcome to the Specific Biblical Truth?
- Does the Integration Plan *match* the Integration Objective with respect to thinking level, Specific Biblical Truth and Academic Content?
- Does the Integration Plan *complement* the academic Lesson Plan or detract from it?
- What question will you ask or statement will you make to integrate the Specific Biblical Truth to the academic Lesson Plan?

Biblical Worldview Integration Planner

1. Subject: Language Arts **Reference(s):** Elements of Literature: First Course; "The Pasture" **Grade:** 7 **Date:** 04/17/08
  Teacher: Kelli Findlay **School:** Cascade Christian Junior High **Contact:** CCS

2. Lesson or Unit Objective/Outcome

underline thinking level and (circle) *academic content*

Students will be able to <u>interpret</u> "The Pasture" as a (possible invitation to take time to enjoy the simple things in life,)

like water springs and calves.

3. Lesson Plan

a) Set *[gets students "set" for learning]*

Play the song "Don't Blink" by Kenny Chesney.

b) Delivery *[outline of lesson plan]*

1. As students listen to the song, ask them to write down words or verses from the song that help them understand the song's message. Write students' ideas on the board.
2. Write students' ideas on the board.
3. Define the literary term "theme." Have students copy this definition in their composition books.
4. Read "The Pasture" on page 324 in their literature books.
5. Ask students to determine what they think the theme of the poem is. Write ideas on the board.
6. Discuss the refrain "I shan't be gone long. --You come too." (Who is "I" and who is "you?")
7. Ask students if they notice any similarities between the poem and the song we listened to at the beginning of the lesson.

c) Closing *[recap, transition or assignment, etc.]*

Have you ever been on vacation with your family or friends and enjoyed a natural wonder" [Recap theme.]

4. Biblical Worldview Component

How does the (academic content) *connect with the bigger picture of:*

☐ GOD
X CREATION
☐ HUMANITY
☐ MORAL ORDER
☐ PURPOSE

Select one.

5. Specific Biblical Truth

to be integrated

Creation is designed to give pleasure to the sight.

6. Biblical Worldview Integration Objective

The students will understand

7. INTEGRATION PLAN

1. Read Genesis 2:9 to the class. [*"And out of the ground the Lord God made every tree grow that is <u>pleasant to the sight</u> and good for food."*]
2. Ask: "What does this verse tell us about creation?" [It is designed to give pleasure to the sight, as well as practical function.]
3. Ask students if they think trees are the only part of creation that God designed for our pleasure. What other created things give pleasure to the sight? [grass, water, leaves, fields...]
4. Read "The Pasture" aloud for a second time. Ask students to point out the "simple" things in the poem that bring pleasure to the sight and refreshment or rejuvenation to the spirit/soul.
5. As students give ideas, reinforce the thought that creation is designed to give pleasure to the sight.

TL: The students will understand

SBT: that creation is designed to give pleasure to the sight,

AC: through the process of reading "The Pasture" and discussing its theme of taking time to enjoy the simple things in life.

8. Post-Lesson Comments:

Biblical Worldview Integration Planner (back page)

Biblical Worldview Focus Question:

How does <u>enjoying the simple things in life</u> **connect with the bigger picture of:**

God *[the nature, character and role of God]?* God's character as a loving Father can be seen in the fact that He designed His handiwork to give us pleasure. [Gen. 2:9]

Creation *[what is made and sustained by God]?* Creation is designed to give pleasure to the sight.

Humanity *[who and what humans are]?* Humans have been made with a capacity to enjoy God's handiwork.

Moral Order *[moral behavior and responsibility]?* We have a responsibility to preserve the simple pleasures of God's creation for others to enjoy.

Purpose *[the intention and meaning of all that exists]?* One of the purposes of God's handiwork is to bring pleasure to human beings.

* *

- **Knowledge:** *list, tell, identify, show, label, collect, examine, tabulate, quote, name,* etc.
- **Comprehension:** *summarize, describe, associate, distinguish, estimate, differentiate, explain in their own words, discuss, articulate,* etc.
- **Application:** *apply, demonstrate, calculate, complete, illustrate, show, solve, modify, relate, change, use, classify, experiment,* etc.
- **Analysis:** *analyze, separate, order, connect, classify, arrange, divide, compare, contrast, select, determine, decipher, predict, interpret, infer,* etc.
- **Synthesis:** *combine, integrate, modify, rearrange, substitute, plan, create, design, invent, compose, formulate, generalize,* etc.
- **Evaluation:** *assess, decide, rank, grade, test, measure, recommend, convince, select, judge, defend, discriminate, support, conclude,* etc.

Step 8: Post-lesson Comments

Defining Integration:

Integration is not	**Integration is not**
_____	_____

OBJECT LESSON *or* INTEGRATION

OBJECT LESSON

1. Illustrates a "lesson" about something _____ the subject matter.

2. Usually takes the form of an _____ or _____.

3. Used to make spiritual lessons more _____, or _____.

4. Reveals the glory of God, purpose of God, or mind of God in relation to something _____ the subject matter itself.

INTEGRATION

1. Directly relates to the _____ itself.

2. Rarely uses analogy or allegory.

3. Used to make the _____ itself more significant.

4. Reveals the glory of God, purpose of God, or mind of God in relation to the _____ itself.

The Worldview Journey*

Four Stages

_____

_____

_____

_____

* Courtesy of Mark Wilson, *Strategic Life Training*, Santa Rosa, California.

Words well said:

*"Whenever Christians make the connection
between faith and life—between the biblical worldview
and the issues of our day—
societies are renewed and communities are restored.*

*And wherever the people of God have committed themselves
to do the will of God, in all spheres and sectors of society,
they have turned the world upside down—
or, better, right side up.*

*Before we can make a real and lasting difference
in the culture, we must understand how the biblical worldview
connects us with every aspect of the creation.*

*This means that we need teachers who are prepared
to help us reconnect with our biblical mandate."*

Chuck Colson
From the Foreword to *Making The Connections*

Worldview Questions
(not an exhaustive list)

Questions about GOD:
- Is there a supernatural Supreme Being?
- If such a Supreme Being exists, is He a personal Being, or an impersonal force? Is He unlimited in power? Is He present everywhere, and does He know everything that is going on?
- Is this God active in human affairs? Does He communicate with mankind? If He does, in what ways can we hear and understand what He is saying?
- Does He love? Is He just? Does He care what happens to people?

Questions about CREATION:
- Did the universe make itself or did a higher Being cause it?
- Is physical matter upheld by the Creator through time or does "Nature" function on its own, independently of God?
- Does the material world have value and meaning? If so, on what basis?
- What is really real, especially in the realm of things I cannot observe or measure?
- Is God an active participant in the world of things He has made and ordained, or is it a "closed system?"

Questions about HUMANITY:
- Were we once fish? Are humans the result of time plus chance plus impersonal matter?
- What determines human worth and value?
- Are people basically good or are they basically corrupt?
- Are people responsible and accountable for their actions or are they caused to behave certain ways by their environment?
- How can people know what is really true and real? Is the human mind capable of knowing what reality truly is? Is observation and measurement the only valid way for humans to determine truth and reality?
- What happens to people after they die?
- Do people have souls? If so, what is a soul?

Questions about MORAL ORDER:
- Is morality a human invention or is it predetermined by God? Is there an ultimate standard of right and wrong to which all humans are subject? If so, what are the rules?
- Is there a right and wrong way to gain and use material resources?
- What is the purpose of the family? What IS a family?
- What is the role of civil government?
- Is there a final judgment? If so, on what basis?

Questions about PURPOSE:
- Does history have any direction? Any meaning?
- Is there a purpose for human existence? If so, what is it?
- Is there a reason for the material world and the resources it contains?
- Has God given any mandates or "job descriptions" for human beings?

Math Connections with the Biblical Worldview
(not an exhaustive list)

Math and God:

- God created all things, and because He did, Math exists.

- God spoke all things into existence, and math is a part of that speech.

- Behind God's speech is God's mind. Math came from that mind, and therefore math reveals that mind.

- Math is reasonable because God is reasonable.

- Math transcends all cultures because God transcends all cultures.

- God is intelligent, and math demonstrates the vastness of that intelligence.

- God is sovereign, ruling over the entire universe. Math is one means by which His rule is implemented.

- God is glorified ["magnified," or "made bigger in our sight"] through math.

Math and Creation:

- Math, being a part of creation, does not exist independently of God. It is "held together" or sustained" continuously through time by Him, and is dependent upon Him for its continuing existence.

- Math, like every other aspect of creation, belongs to God.

- Math, as every other part of creation, is subject to God's authority.

- Math is constantly speaking to us of the fact that we live in a created, intelligently governed world.

Math and Humanity:

- Humanity needs math as a tool for fulfilling God's First Commission of Genesis 1:26-28.

- The ability to use math for problem solving is a remarkable gift to humanity from God. Any person who uses math to solve a problem or to create something is exercising a marvelous gift from God.

- Math is a constant reminder that humanity is created in the likeness and image of God, capable of abstract reasoning and creative invention.

- Math is able to instill patience, persistence and character in humans.

- Math, when seen for what it really is, can radically affect a person's attitude toward God, and thus it is able to promote spiritual growth. Seeing the glory of God in math changes people.

- Humanity is able to creatively and intelligently label and name the mathematical language God put in place. This naming process is a part of what it means to rule over the earth, and such labeling continues to go on.

- Humanity must live in harmony with math, or pain may result.

Math and Moral Order:

- Math can be used for good or evil, as it is applied in the fields of science, technology, economics, sociology, etc.

- Math is a demonstration of the existence of objective truths. Things that are truly "right" and "wrong" do exist in the created, ordered universe, and math reminds us of this fact.

- Math demonstrates the law of non-contradiction: "two answers which are mutually exclusive cannot both be true at the same time in the same sense."

Math and Purpose:

- Math equips us to fulfill the First Commission of Genesis 1:26-28.

- Math enables us to bring order to disorder, to invent, and to shape things into new things. When we do this in a way that honors the Lord, we glorify Him and bring benefit to ourselves and others.

- Math helps us to fulfill the Great Commission of Matthew 28:18-20, through such math-enabled inventions as the radio, TV, computers, Internet, modes of transportation, and inventions yet to be made using yet-to-be-discovered math.

- Math enables us to glorify God by doing the "good works which He has ordained" [Ephesians 2:10] more effectively. [Consider the fields of medicine, agriculture, economics, etc.]

The Five Worldview Components Defined

"GOD" has to do with the nature, character and role of God.

GOD is a divine Person, with mind, emotion and free will. (Isaiah 1:18; Psalms 115:3)

GOD is omnipotent, omniscient and omnipresent. (Hebrews 1:3, Psalms 139)

GOD is sovereign over all things. (Psalms 83:18)

GOD communicates with humanity. (Romans 1:18-21, II Timothy 3:16, John 8:26-29)

GOD is faultless in judgment, infinite in mercy and perfect in justice. (I John 4:12)

"CREATION" has to do with what is made and sustained by God.

ALL THINGS have been created and are sustained by God. (Col. 1:16-17)

THE REALM OF CREATION belongs entirely to God. (Psalms 24:1)

THE CREATED REALM includes physical and spiritual realities, as well as temporal and eternal realities. (Colossians 1:16-17, I John 2:17)

CREATION has been plagued by sin since the Fall of humanity. (Genesis 3-6)

THE CREATED REALM has not been forsaken by God, in spite of the Fall. (John 3:16)

"HUMANITY" has to do with who and what humans are.

HUMANS were created by God's choice and design. (Genesis 1:26-28)

MAN AND WOMAN were specially created in the likeness and image of God so they could engage in His purposes. (Genesis 1:26-28, 9:6)

PEOPLE are alienated from God through sin. (Isaiah 53:6, Romans 5:12)

HUMANS are restored to a relationship with God through Christ. (Romans. 6, 7, 8)

ALL HUMANS experience physical death, followed by eternal fellowship with God or eternal separation from Him. (Hebrews 9:27, John 3:16)

"MORAL ORDER" has to do with moral behavior and responsibility.

MORAL ORDER is determined by God, not invented by humans. (Exodus 20:1-17)

The MORAL ORDER of God is non-optional, and non-negotiable. (Romans 1, 6, and 7)

MORAL ORDER, when violated, requires consequences. (Romans 6:23)

MORAL ORDER is clarified through biblical examples of good and evil. (Psalms 19:7)

MORAL ORDER is upheld through God's ordained institutions of family, church and civil government. (Genesis 2:21-24, Romans 13:1-7, Matthew 16-18)

"PURPOSE" has to do with the intention or meaning of all that exists.

The FIRST COMMISSION was that of rulership over the earth. (Gen. 1:26-28)

The WILL of God is to be done on earth, as it is in heaven. (Matthew 6:10)

The FUNCTION of believers in Christ is to be the "salt of the earth" and the "light of the world". (Matthew 5:13-14)

The PURPOSE for all things centers in Christ. (Colossians 1:16-18)

The GREAT COMMISSION is still in place. (Matthew 28:18-20)

STEP 2: ACADEMIC OBJECTIVE

1. Is the _thinking level_ of the lesson objective/outcome clear? (Underline)

2. Is the main (content) of the lesson clear? (Circle)

STEP 4: BIBLICAL WORLDVIEW COMPONENT – FOCUS QUESTION

1. Has the academic content been specified in the Focus Question?

2. Has the focus question been narrowed down to ONE of the five Worldview Components?

3. Does the selected Biblical Worldview Component connect logically and naturally to the academic content, or is it a "stretch"?

STEP 5: SPECIFIC BIBLICAL TRUTH

1. Does the Specific Biblical Truth answer the "what about" question, with respect to the selected Biblical Worldview Component?

STEP 6: BIBLICAL WORLDVIEW INTEGRATION OBJECTIVE

1. Does the _thinking level_ specified in the Integration Objective match (or not supercede) the _thinking level_ specified in the Lesson Objective?

2. Is the Specific Biblical Truth included in the Integration Objective?

3. Does the (content) of the Integration Objective match the (content) of the Lesson Objective?

STEP 7: INTEGRATION PLAN

1. Does the Integration Plan match the Integration Objective with respect to _thinking level, specific biblical truth_ and _academic content_?

2. Does the Integration Plan complement the academic Lesson Objective or detract from it?

3. What question will you ask or statement will you make to integrate the specific biblical truth to the academic lesson?

Bibliography and Resources

Books:

All Truth is God's Truth, by Arthur Holmes
Assumptions That Affect Our Lives, by Christian Overman
Biblical Integration: Understanding the World Through The Word, by Mark Eckel
Creation Regained, by Albert Wolters
The Christian Mind, by Harry Blamires
How Now Shall We Live? by Charles Colson and Nancy Pearcey
How Shall We Then Live? by Francis Schaeffer
Kingdom Education: God's Plan for Educating Future Generations, by Glen Schultz
Kingdoms in Conflict, by Ronald Nash
Making Sense of Your World, by William Brown and Gary Phillips
Reclaiming The Future of Christian Education: A Transforming Vision, by Albert E. Greene, Jr.
The Transforming Vision, by Brian Walsh and Richard Middleton
Thinking and Acting Like a Christian, by Bruce Lockerbie
The Universe Next Door, by James Sire
Total Truth, by Nancy Pearcey
Passing the Baton, by Jeff Meyer

Organizations:

The Biblical Worldview Institute www.biblicalworldviewinstitute.org
Worldview Matters www.biblicalworldview.com
Probe Ministries www.probe.org
Worldview Academy www.worldview.org
Summit Ministries www.summit.org
Summit at Bryan College www.bryan.edu
Cornerstone Curriculum www.cornerstonecurriculum.com
Strategic Life Training www.strategiclifetraining.com
Focus on the Family's The Truth Project www.thetruthproject.org
Ravi Zacharias International Ministries www.rzim.org

© 2008 *The Biblical Worldview Institute*   31

Biblical Worldview Integration Planner

1. Subject : _____
Teacher: _____

Reference(s): _____
School: _____

Date: _____
Grade: _____
Contact: _____

2. Lesson or Unit Objective/Outcome
<u>underline</u> thinking level and (circle) academic content

3. Lesson Plan
a) Set *[gets students "set" for learning]*

b) Delivery *[outline of lesson plan]*

c) Closing *[recap, transition or assignment, etc.]*

4. Biblical Worldview Component

How does the (academic content) connect with the bigger picture of:

☐ GOD
☐ CREATION
☐ HUMANITY
☐ MORAL ORDER
☐ PURPOSE

Select one.

5. Specific Biblical Truth
to be integrated

6. Biblical Worldview Integration Objective

7. INTEGRATION PLAN

TL:

SBT:

AC:

8. Post-Lesson Comments:

© 2008 *The Biblical Worldview Institute, Puyallup, WA, USA*

© **2008** *The Biblical Worldview Institute*

Biblical Worldview Integration Planner (back page)

Biblical Worldview Focus Question:

How does _____ connect with the bigger picture of

(the Academic Content of this lesson)

God [the nature, character and role of God]?

Creation [what is made and sustained by God]?

Humanity [who and what humans are]?

Moral Order [moral behavior and responsibility]?

Purpose [the intention and meaning of all that exists]?

* *

- **Knowledge:** *list, tell, identify, show, label, collect, examine, tabulate, quote, name, etc.*
- **Comprehension:** *summarize, describe, associate, distinguish, estimate, differentiate, explain in their own words, discuss, articulate, etc.*
- **Application:** *apply, demonstrate, calculate, complete, illustrate, show, solve, modify, relate, change, use, classify, experiment, etc.*
- **Analysis:** *analyze, separate, order, connect, classify, arrange, divide, compare, contrast, select, determine, decipher, predict, interpret, infer, etc.*
- **Synthesis:** *combine, integrate, modify, rearrange, substitute, plan, create, design, invent, compose, formulate, generalize, etc.*
- **Evaluation:** *assess, decide, rank, grade, test, measure, recommend, convince, select, judge, defend, discriminate, support, conclude, etc.*

© 2008 *The Biblical Worldview Institute* 33